Let Me
Explain

A Story about Donor Insemination

Let Me Explain

A Story about Donor Insemination

by
Jane T. Schnitter

Perspectives Press
Indianapolis, Indiana

Illustrated by Joanne Bowring

Perspectives Press
P.O. Box 90318
Indianapolis, IN 46290-0318
U.S.A.

Manufactured in the United States of America
ISBN 0-944934-12-9

Library of Congress Cataloging-in-Publication Data

Schnitter, Jane T., 1958-
      Let me explain: a story about donor insemination / by Jane T.
Schnitter; illustrated by Joanne Bowring.
            p.   cm.
      Summary: A little girl explains how she was conceived through
artificial insemination and that although she has genes from her
mother and a donor, her dad is her only father.
      ISBN 0-944934-12-9
      1. Artificial insemination, Human--Juvenile literature. 2. Father
and child--Juvenile literature. [1. Artificial insemination,
Human. 2. Father and child. 3. Genetics.] I. Bowring, Joanne,
ill. II. Title.
HQ761.S36   1995
306.874'2--dc20
                                                                94-41737
                                                                      CIP
                                                                      AC

I would like you to meet someone very special. The best homework helper, strongest jar opener, and the fastest person ever to spray me with a hose...my dad.

He was there when I was growing inside my mom, and he liked to put his hand on her huge tummy and feel me kick.

He watched when I first sat up.
I bit him with my first tooth.
He caught me when I fell after my first steps.

Of course, I can't remember any of that. Dad told me about it, so I know it's true, because he has pictures of everything.

I *can* remember a lot of things, though. When I was little, Dad always held my hand tightly when we crossed the street. He still tries to hold my hand...although I'm old enough to cross the street myself.

He watches me at every softball game and cheers louder than any other parent. (Sometimes he embarrasses me when he cheers so loud.)

My dad helps me be the best that I can be.

My dad bought me my first bike. It was a little blue bike with long tassels hanging from the handles. He taught me how to ride that bike. Every night, after dinner, he would run beside me as I pedaled, making sure I didn't fall.

Now I have a bigger bike and I'm a good bike rider. Dad and I go on trail rides together. Sometimes, Mom joins us. We have lots of fun on our bikes.

Things aren't always perfect, though. I'm supposed to take out the trash and dry the dishes. When I forget to do my chores, sometimes Dad's the one who talks to me about it or sends me to my room. If my bike is still outside when he comes home from work, he reminds me to put it away.

Sometimes we get mad at each other, but there's one thing I know...

Cheering me on, helping me out, or correcting me, he's my dad.

Dad taught me to ride

Lots of whipped cream

Ay dad and I are a lot alike. At night, for a snack,
we love to eat Fudge Ripple ice cream. Dad makes us sundaes
with lots of whipped cream and a red cherry on the very
top. We smack our lips and lick our spoons as we eat
our snack together.

Sometimes, after our snack, we play cards. Dad taught me
how to play rummy. We sit with our cards held tightly in our
hands, each of us trying to win. We have lots of fun. Whoever
wins the last hand puts the cards away. I'm a very good
player. I always win the last hand.

After the last hand, Dad always says, "Oh, Baloney!"
Whenever my dad thinks something is silly, he says, "Oh,
Baloney!"
I say, "Oh, Baloney!" a lot, too.

When football is on television, you'll find us both cheering for our team, because we both love football. When our team scores a touchdown, Dad and I hop out of our chairs. Then we do a little touchdown dance we made up.

My mom says my dad and I are two of a kind except for one thing. We don't look anything alike. And I know why. It's because we don't have the same genes. This is where it starts to get confusing.

I didn't know about *genes* and you've probably never heard of them before either, but my mom and dad told me all about them, and I'll explain them to you.

First of all, everyone has genes, and I don't mean the blue jeans that people like to wear. Genes are tiny. I mean really tiny. You need a powerful microscope to see them at all. Genes live in the cells of your body, and they are very important.

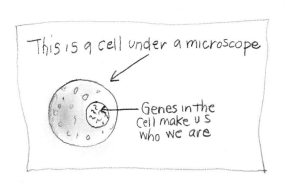

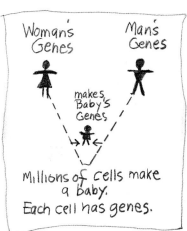

Genes decide what color your hair and eyes and skin will be. They decide if you will be tall or short or in between. Will you have curly, wavy or straight hair? Teeth that need braces? Genes decide this, too.

How big will your nose grow? Your genes know!

Do your earlobes hang down or are they connected tight to your head? Mine hang down, and my genes decided that.

My genes also gave me my big feet. Genes even decide if you will be a boy or a girl, so you can see how important they are.

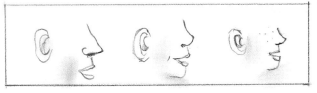

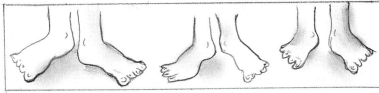

But genes don't only decide what you will look like. They also can help determine your interests and talents. Do you draw well, or is music what you do best? Can you run very fast or jump very high? Are you a whiz in math or are you better at dancing? Would you rather spend your time reading a book or jumping rope?

Genes can make things easier or harder for you to learn.

Of course, if you don't even try something, you won't know if you could be good at it. And you have to work hard and practice to be really good at anything, but genes kind of give you a push.

My genes gave me a good sense of balance and long legs. These things help me play softball and ride my bike. But practicing with my dad made me so good at scoring runs that I was my league's highest scorer! And without good balance, it would have taken a lot longer for my dad to help me learn to ride my bike. Why, without good balance, I might not enjoy trail riding as much as I do!

13

Now that you know all about genes, I know what your next question is, because it was my question, too.

Where do genes come from?

My parents told me all about it!   Let me explain...

Women have something inside of them called *ova*. These are tiny, tiny eggs located in their *ovaries*, next to the *uterus* where babies grow. You can't see ova with your eyes, but they are full of genes.

Men have *sperm* inside their *testicles*. These also are tiny, even tinier than the ova, but they are full of his genes.

When the *ova* from one woman and the *sperm* from the one man get together, a really wonderful thing can happen. A baby may start to grow. That baby gets its own genes from the genes in both the ova and the sperm that got together to make him or her grow.

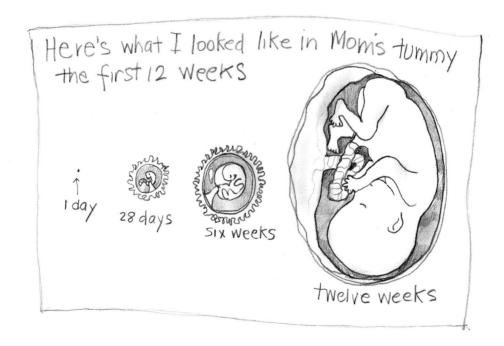

Here's what I looked like in Mom's tummy the first 12 weeks

1 day

28 days

six weeks

twelve weeks

Everybody in the whole world starts out that way.

We just all have different genes.

My eyes are chestnut brown. So are my mom's. My mom can play the piano really well, and you know something, I play pretty well myself. I get some of my genes from my mom, so it isn't surprising that I look like her and have some of her talents.

But I don't have any genes from my dad because I didn't come from his sperm. His sperm don't work the way they need to make a baby grow. I act like my dad sometimes though, watching football, riding bikes, playing rummy, or saying, "Oh Baloney!" That's because I've learned these things from him, not because I have his genes on the inside.

Learning about genes explains a lot of things, but it also brought up a lot of questions. I'm sure you have some of the same questions.

Questions like:

What was wrong with my dad's sperm?

Does it make him sick?

Does he go to the doctor about it?

Can something like this happen to me when I want a baby?

I wanted to know more, so I asked my dad. Dad thought a minute and then he answered.

"Do you remember last summer when your bicycle chain wouldn't work?"

I thought back. Sure, I remembered, but it didn't seem to have anything to do with Dad's sperm. My bike chain wasn't working. Dad and I tried to fix it, but couldn't. Finally, we brought it to the repair shop. They tried to fix it, too, but it still wouldn't work. Even though they couldn't find a reason why it didn't work, I still had to get a new bike chain.

"Exactly!" said my dad, nodding his head.

It still didn't make sense, but I know my dad. He always explains things until I understand. I waited for him to explain further.

This is what he told me.

First of all, it can happen to anyone. That doesn't mean it will happen, but just that it could. It's sad, but it doesn't make you bad or strange. No one is perfect.

If something like this happens when I'm married and try to have a baby, I'll be sad at first, just like my dad and mom were. But I'll know at least one solution. I could do exactly what they did to have a baby. And they had me, so you can see how good it turned out. Dad said they were so happy when they learned I was going to be born, they couldn't quit smiling for a whole week.

What did they do to have me, you ask?

That's what I asked, too. Let me explain…

When Dad and Mom first wanted a baby, they tried on their own, with his sperm and her ova. That didn't seem to work. (Kind of like when I tried to work on my own bike chain.) They went to doctors to see if they could figure out what the problem was. (Kind of like the repair shop for my bike.) After testing both Mom and Dad, the doctors discovered the problem was with my dad's sperm.

The doctor doesn't know why, but my dad's body can't make sperm that make babies. He had to come up with different sperm for a baby to grow. (Kind of like getting my new bike chain to make my bike work.)

I was beginning to understand, except for one very important question that I'm sure you have right now.

"Different sperm?" you ask. "Is that possible? It sounds weird."

I had the same question. My dad helped me answer it. It isn't like running to the store to buy a new bike chain.

Let me explain…

You know if someone's legs don't work, then they may use a wheelchair to get around. We've all seen people in wheelchairs. And if someone has trouble seeing clearly, they may wear glasses. You may even wear glasses yourself.

That all makes sense, but where do you get new sperm? Where did half of my genes come from?

I'll explain that too.

There is something called *donor insemination.*

Whew! That's a mouthful! You don't have to remember it though, because there's not going to be a test. It's just good to hear what it's called.

My parents shortened it to *D.I.*

It means…a man gives sperm so someone else can make a baby. The man is called a donor because he donates his sperm to make a baby, but the baby doesn't belong to him. In fact, he usually doesn't even know which parents use his sperm.

Still confused? Let me explain…

They can't put new sperm in a man's body, but they can put a donor's sperm with a woman's ova to make a baby grow. Then that woman, with her husband, become the baby's parents.

That is what my mom and dad did.

Someone else's sperm, with Mom's ova, started me growing.

That's the way Mom was able to have a baby grow inside of her. That baby was me. Dad was there the whole time I was growing inside of Mom and he was there when I was born. He says it worked out perfectly since he got me. I have to agree with him, since I got him for a dad.

But I still had a question.

Whose sperm did I come from?

Dad had an answer for that, but it was not the answer I wanted to hear.

He doesn't know!

He knows a lot about the donor and he told me everything he could. He knows the color of his eyes and skin and hair. He knows how tall he is and his nationality and how much he weighs.

Sometimes parents know more than this, but hardly any parents can answer all the questions a kid might have.

Questions like...Is he funny or is he serious?

Does he have three dogs and two cats and a bird?

Does he like sports?

I don't know any of those things because my mom and dad don't know them either.

Will I ever meet the donor?

Dad says probably not. It usually doesn't work that way. It would be hard to find him because we don't really know whose sperm it was. And he isn't going to show up on my doorstep one day because he doesn't know who we are either. I got his genes and that's an important part of who I am, but he's not my dad.

I think, though, that I'm always going to wonder a little about what he's like.

Does all this make me different?

NO! It doesn't make me any different or any more special than anyone else in the world.

It's part of who I am. I still like ice cream and football and bike riding. I still stink in spelling and I can still play the piano. I still have brown hair and brown eyes and big feet. I still want to be a teacher when I grow up.

No, wait, I mean a doctor...or maybe a musician.

Heck, I still don't know what I want to be when I grow up.

And I still love my dad.

My dad is slightly bald, and he loves
to tell me jokes.

He wears glasses to read, has stinky feet,
and when he laughs, everyone else has to
laugh, too.

He gives great hugs.

I can see him right now, sleeping
in his favorite chair. In a few minutes,
I'll wake him up and we're going
on a bike ride.

W hat the whole thing comes down to is this…

The sperm came from someone else, but once
that wonderful baby started to grow,
(Me! Remember?), there was only one dad.

My dad.

The dad who liked to put his hand on Mom's
tummy and feel me kick. The dad who
watched me first sit up, bled when I tried out
my first tooth on him, and always caught me
when I fell.

He still does.

After all, he's my dad.

About the author

Jane Schnitter was born and raised in Hamburg, New York. She married Paul, her high school sweetheart, and then moved to Ohio where she attended Ohio University. Her husband's job soon had them moving again. After living in Pennsylvania, New Jersey, and North Carolina, they settled once more in Ohio, just outside of Columbus. Over the years, the Schnitters adopted two boys, had two girls by birth and had eight foster children.

Besides her writing, Jane also volunteers in the local school, is PTA president, and tries to keep up with the many activities of her four children, Paul Jr., Corey, Emily and Megan. Jane's other works include *William Is My Brother* (Perspectives Press, 1991.)

About the illustrator

Joanne Bowring has been an artist and illustrator for 20 years. She illustrates middle school textbooks and children's books, including self publishing *Mr. Fuzzy H.U.G.S.* along with the author. She has illustrated several books for Perspectives Press including *Real for Sure Sister, Where the Sun Kisses the Sea,* and *Two Birthdays for Beth.*

Joanne enjoys volunteering for children in the local grade school in a program to get their own books and poetry published. Joanne lives in Wauwatosa, Wisconsin, with her husband, Doug, and children, Mary and Tim.

LET US INTRODUCE OURSELVES

Since 1982 Perspectives Press has focused primarily on infertility, adoption, and related reproductive and child welfare issues. Our purpose is to promote understanding of these issues and to educate and sensitize those personally experiencing these life situations, professionals who work in these fields and the public at large. Our titles are never duplicative or competitive with material already available through traditional publishers. We seek to find and fill only niches which are empty. In addition to this book, our current titles include

FOR ADULTS

Perspectives on a Grafted Tree

Understanding: A Guide to Impaired Fertility for Family and Friends

Sweet Grapes: How to Stop Being Infertile and Start Living Again

Residential Treatment: A Tapestry of Many Therapies

A Child's Journey through Placement

Adopting after Infertility

Taking Charge of Infertility

Flight of the Stork

FOR CHILDREN

Our Baby: A Birth and Adoption Story

The Mulberry Bird: Story of an Adoption

Real for Sure Sister

Filling in the Blanks: A Guided Look at Growing Up Adopted

Where the Sun Kisses the Sea

William Is My Brother

Lucy's Feet

Let Me Explain: A Story about Donor Insemination

Two Birthdays for Beth

If you are writing on our issues, we invite you to contact us with SASE to request our writer's guidelines, which will help you to determine whether your idea might fit into our publishing plans.

Perspectives Press
P.O. Box 90318
Indianapolis, IN 46290-0318
U.S.A.